THE SILVEY-JEX PARTNERSHIP

Dalesman

Dalesman Publishing Company
Stable Courtyard, Broughton Hall, Skipton, North Yorkshire BD23 3AZ

First Edition 1998

© Silvey-Jex Partnership 1998

A British Library Cataloguing in Publication record is available for this book

ISBN 1 85568 151 X

Also by Silvey-Jex Outdoor Wreckreations (ISBN 1 85568 104 8)
and Growing Pains (ISBN 1 85568 115 3)

Printed by Midas Printing (HK) Ltd

The English Countryside as seen by the Silvey Jex Partnership

AAH...DON'T YOU JUST LOVE THOSE COUNTRY SMELLS?

EVENING LADS... BEEN SCARING THE PANTS OFF THE HIKERS AGAIN?

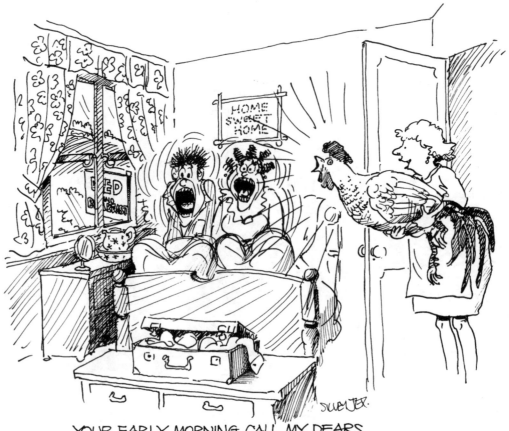

YOUR EARLY MORNING CALL MY DEARS

WOODWORM YOU SAY...NO I'VE NEVER SEEN ANY WOODWORM

WE'RE TOGETHER

DON'T BE SILLY DEAR ... THERE'S NO WAY THEY CAN CLIMB ONTO THE ROOF

I DUNNO GEORGE...I RECKON THAT OLD PIG OF YOUR'N GITS DAFTER 'N DAFTER

RIGHT! YOU'RE THE FAMILY WHO ORDERED PORK—WHICH BITS DO YOU WANT?

MUST BE A PRETTY PROSPEROUS AREA AROUND HERE
—THAT'S A CAMEL HAIR COAT HE'S WEARING

DON'T YOU WORRY ABOUT THE OLD VILLAGE IDIOT...
YOU CARRY ON CANOODLING LIKE I'M NOT HERE.

CAN'T YOU FORGET THE OFFICE FOR 5 MINUTES?

MIND THOSE SHEEP - LOOK OUT FOR THAT BEND - WATCH OUT FOR THAT RABBIT - DON'T GO SO FAST - SLOW DOWN . . . .

THAT'S IT MOTHER .. GEORGE IS RIGHT BEHIND Y....

TELL IT WE'RE VEGETARIANS

AAH....DID YOU SEE THAT FRANK?...A CUTE LITTLE FOX

"OH LOOK" HE SAID "MUCK SPREADING—LET'S STOP AND WATCH"

...THEN, YOU BOILS 'EM UP WITH SUGAR IN A PRESERVING PAN, LET'S IT SET AND YOU GET'S THE PRETTIEST PINK JELLY YOU EVER DID SEE. A 'COURSE, IT'S POISONOUS MIND

ARE YOU PUTTING IT UP...OR TAKING IT DOWN?

NEVER MIND "MANURE FOR THE BEANS" THAT'S HIS NEW BUCKET AND SPADE

NEXT TIME WE GO FOR A WALK IN THE COUNTRY...IT WOULD BE NICE TO SEE SOME OF IT.

NOT QUITE AS ROOMY AS THE VOLVO ESTATE – BUT AS LONG AS YOU'RE HAPPY

ARE EARWIGS POISONOUS?

OH YES... PART OF THE FURNITURE IS OLD HARRY

"PULL!"

THAT'S RIGHT...TIS FRIABLE, CHEMICAL-FREE, COMPLETELY ORGANIC HUMUS.
WHAT WE IN THE BUSINESS CALLS ... PIG-SHIT.

AAH! THAT MUST BE ONE OF THEM "OFF THE ROAD" VEHICLES

HURRY UP DEAR... THERE'LL BE SOMEBODY ALONG ANY MINUTE

OOOH..."THROWING THE WELLIE" HAS STARTED...MUSN'T MISS THAT.

...AND AT THE BACK WE HAVE A NEAT LITTLE CHEMICAL TOILET

THIS IS THE ONE WE'RE FELLING LADY

I WOULD'T TOUGH IT WITH A BARGE-POLE MYSELF

THEY TELL ME THE AREA ROUND HERE IS PRONE TO SUDDEN FLOODING?

DO BE CAREFUL SIR - THE SOAKAWAY FOR THE OLD SEPTIC TANK IS JUST ABOUT........

THAT BE THE ORIGINAL CORRUGATED IRON, THAT BE

WELL...THE FOOTSIE'S DOWN A COUPLE OF POINTS, THE BOTTOM'S DROPPED OUT OF COMMODITIES IN FACT MY BROKER SAYS THAT....WHOOPS...HOLD ON..TOURISTS. BETTER "OO-AR" FOR A WHILE

SORRY LAD...BUT MUSTN'T OVERLOAD THE TRACTOR

THERE'S NOTHING GOES BETTER WITH A PORK FAT 'N PIGS BLOOD PUDDING
MY DEARS... THAN A NICE GLASS OF HOME MADE BROCCOLI WINE

MUM! .... DAD'S STUCK IN THE KISSING GATE WITH A LADY

YES, OLD TOM MAKES A FORTUNE OUT OF MANURE — NO FLIES ON HIM.... WELL, ONE OR TWO MAYBE

YOU ASKED THE MAN FOR STRAW FOR YOUR RABBIT... YOU CARRY IT

ONE DAY SON—ALL THIS MUD, FILTH AND STENCH...WILL BE YOURS

OH NO...NOT YOUR FATHERS "YARD OF ALE - DOWN IN ONE" TRICK AGAIN

...IT'S FOR YOU THELMA

WE'LL GIVE HIM ANOTHER HALF AN HOUR AND THEN WE'LL CALL IT A NIGHT.

MUM! WHAT SORT OF MARKINGS DOES AN ADDER HAVE?

...LUCY....JENNIFER...

DAMMIT...THAT WERE A GOOD WATCH THAT WERE

'TIS NO WONDER IT WON'T GO... YOU GOT IT UPSIDE DOWN SIR

DON'T PANIC BRIAN.... KEEP TELLING YOURSELF "IT'S JUST A COW PAT"

EXCUSE ME... BUT YOU'RE SITTING IN THE MIDDLE OF MY MOTORWAY

EAT UP...DON'T WANT THOSE NASTY OLD ANTS TO GET IT DO WE?

I DON'T SEE THE PROBLEM... IT'S NOT AS THOUGH SHE'S CARRYING A BACK PACK OR ANYTHING

DON'T YOU WORRY ABOUT A THING LOVE...I'VE GOT YOUR HANDBAG

NO IT'S NOT AN ACCIDENT OFFICER...THE SINK'S BLOCKED

WE'LL JUST WAIT A MOMENT WHILE YOUR FATHER CROSSES THE CATTLE GRID

BLIMEY—WE MIGHT JUST AS WELL HAVE STAYED AT HOME

NON-STOP BLACKBERRYING

THAT'S WHAT YOU GET WHEN YOU CALL A MORRIS DANCER A BIG GIRLS BLOUSE

RIGHT...ARE WE ALL READY TO IMPRESS THE NEIGHBOURS?

I'VE CHANGED MY MIND... IT'S RAINING

STRANGE...THIS ONE'S ONLY GOT ONE TEAT

ER... DOREEN... ARE YOU SURE YOU PICKED UP THE RIGHT BACK-PACK WHEN WE LEFT THE HOSTEL?

WELL IT'S NOT <u>MY</u> IDEA OF A WALKING HOLIDAY

QUICK DARREN, GO AND STOP YOUR DAD YODELLING
HE'LL WAKE UP THE ENTIRE LAKE DISTRICT

THAT'S THE LAST TIME WE SET FOOT IN THE COUNTRYSIDE